It's not Magic but it Could Be

Tips, tricks and sciency bits to manage anxiety

Dedicated to Haylee, Oliver and Aiva. You are my everything.

First self-published and printed November 2021

ISBN 978-1-914408-96-0

Printed in UK

Contact: James@it'snotmagicbutitcouldbe.com

It was mid-morning on a Monday. The sun was shining, the sky was as blue as lapis lazuli, and was completely cloud-free. Days like these put a smile on your face and a spring in your step. And when you went to school somewhere as majestic and mystical as Stormy Skies Magic Academy, it was almost impossible not to buzz with excitement.

ut not everyone was buzzing. Or even smiling, for that matter. Down by the central fountain sat a red-haired, freckly young witch called Rose. Her face was as gloomy as a rain cloud and she seemed oblivious to the glorious weather and the merry sound of birds chirruping overhead. There was only one thing on Rose's mind, and that thing was the Year 8 spell-casting exam the very next day. It was an important exam and as such, all the pupils had been given a study day in order to prepare for it.

Rose was usually full of beans and wore a great big grin wherever she went. She loved her

school, she had lots of friends and was pretty good at most of her subjects too, including spell-casting. The trouble was, she always got so nervous about tests and exams that the very thought of them gave her a tummy ache. And when she felt like this, she found it almost impossible to concentrate on studying or to remember all the things she had learnt in class. She simply flew into a blind panic and everything jumbled up in her brain. Her potions teacher said that it was probably anxiety but Rose didn't really know what that meant or what she was supposed to do about it. Giving her troubles a name didn't solve them.

The half-hourly chime of the central clock tower gave Rose a start and, when she looked up, she saw her good friend, Arlo, walking over, his usual cheeky grin spread across his face. Despite being in year 10, Rose and Arlo had been friends for ever, and often hung out together at lunch and break times.

As soon as Arlo saw Rose's face and the discarded, half-eaten packet of witch crisps, he knew something was up, even though she assured him that she was just fine. But, luckily, Arlo knew his friend very well, so he was not fooled! Since she did not seem to be her usual cheery self, he decided to see if there was anything he could do to help. He actually had a pretty good idea what the problem was. He had seen her like this before.

"I've got my spell-casting exam tomorrow too," said Arlo. "I'm really nervous. How are you feeling about yours?"

"Petrified!" Rose replied.

"I know you'll do great," said Arlo. "But telling you that doesn't really help, I suppose, does it?"

"Not really," said Rose, "but thanks for trying."

Arlo went quiet for a minute or two, and when he spoke again, he had completely changed the subject. A little frown appeared on his forehead, just below his jet black fringe, then he then wrinkled up his nose and asked Rose a question.

"What's that smell?" said Arlo.

"Um, I can't smell anything!" Rose replied, a bit puzzled.

"Sure, you can," said Arlo. "Have a good old sniff."

So Rose gave it another ago and soon realised that if she concentrated, she could smell all sorts of things.

"Well," she began, "I think I can smell my crisps a bit, and there is definitely something stinky coming from the greenhouse."

"Hmmmm, interesting," said Arlo, stroking his chin and looking all serious. "Speaking of crisps, what do yours taste like?" Rose couldn't think of how to describe them so she picked up a hat-shaped crisp and popped it into her mouth. She closed her eyes so she could concentrate better.

"They are salty, crunchy, oh, and they have a hint of spice," said Rose.

"Sounds yummy," smiled Arlo. "And now, I have one final question; can you hear anything?"

"Well, apart from you asking me strange questions, I can hear the birds chirruping above us and the fountain splashing. What's this all about, Arlo? You know that if you want one of my crisps, all you have to do is ask!"

"Ahh," said Arlo, with such a flair of expression that you would think he was about

to reveal the answer to an ancient wizarding secret, "well, were you thinking about that spell exam at all when you were focussing on your sense of smell, taste and hearing?"

"You said no more questions!" replied Rose, half-jokingly as she started to realise what Arlo was getting at. "I guess I wasn't, no."

"Exactly!" cried the young wizard. "I learnt this trick last year. It's called 'getting grounded', but not in the 'no computer games or playing with toads for a week' kind of way. It's a kind of mindfulness, which is a way to help you keep your thoughts in the present moment and not on the future or on the past because this can sometimes make you anxious or sad." Rose had heard the expression 'mindfulness' before but until now had never really understood what it meant.

She thanked Arlo for telling her about mindfulness and explaining about getting grounded. And promised herself that she would try this trick in future whenever she felt worried or anxious or sad and maybe try to find some more mindful activities that she might enjoy too.

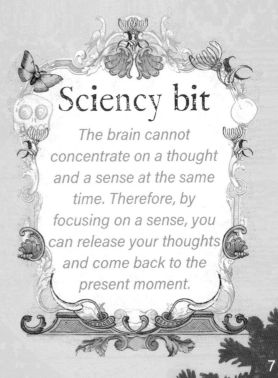

Sciency bit

The brain cannot concentrate on a thought and a sense at the same time. Therefore, by focusing on a sense, you can release your thoughts and come back to the present moment.

"ome on, race you to the hallway of mirrors!" said Arlo suddenly. And before Rose could say anything, they were both sprinting through the school gardens to the east side of the main building.

Five minutes later, both witch and wizard were standing outside a large set of wooden doors. They

were grinning from ear to ear and panting hard after their run.

"How do you ... feel after ... that run?" asked Arlo between breaths.

"Pretty ... good actually. In fact. . . I think I feel better than I did before it," said Rose.

"Ah, ha," smiled Arlo, "I thought you might! Does it feel like the exercise has cleared your head a bit?"

"Yes," replied Rose. "That's exactly what it feels like."

Then Arlo told Rose that when he was in Year 7 he used to really struggle with anxiety too and that he used to feel himself bubble up with worry like a bottle of fizzy pop. But then his sports teacher suggested that he use exercise to get rid of his nervous energy and clear his head of his worries.

"I never knew you had anxiety," said Rose in surprise.

"Yep," answered her friend, "but I asked around for ideas to help me manage it, and then I used the ones I liked best. Exercise is my favourite and it really works for me. I feel so calm and refreshed afterwards".

"Wow!" said Rose. "I never knew that. What's strange," she continued, "is that I know I'm actually quite good at spell-casting, but I'm still worried about the exam tomorrow. I wonder why that is?"

Sciency bit

When we get anxious, our bodies produce adrenalin. Exercise helps to use up this adrenalin leaving us feeling calmer and more relaxed. It also creates feel good chemicals called endorphins, which naturally make us feel a bit happier.

"That's exactly why we're here," said Arlo, taking Rose by the hand and leading her inside the east wing and down a long mirrored corridor. Rose noticed that each mirror had a little name plaque above it. But the really bizarre thing was that each mirror showed a different reflection of her as she walked past.

"Here we are," said Arlo as they stopped by a mirror with a plaque which read 'my brain'. "This mirror will help to show you how your brain works and what happens in it when you get scared or anxious."

"So, is this what my brain looks like?" said Rose, finding it hard to believe what she was seeing. But before Arlo could answer, Professor Jackdaw rounded the corner, giving both children a fright. Out of the corner of her eye, Rose noticed that the reflection in the mirror had suddenly changed, and little flashing dots had appeared at the bottom of the image.

Professor Jackdaw actually
taught Rose in Magical History.
And although she looked a bit scary when
accompanied by her scruffy looking pet crow,
was actually one of the kindest teachers Rose
had ever met.

Brain

Upper part
of the brain

Lower part
of the brain

Information
passed by neurons

After apologising for giving the pair a fright, Professor Jackdaw confirmed that the mirror did indeed show the inside of Rose's brain, and the flashing dots were actually pieces of information being passed around the brain by tiny cells called neurons. The fact that the dots had appeared in the lower part of the brain meant that Rose had reacted fearfully to to the Professors unexpected appearance. Rose went on to explain what they were doing there and, as she started talking about the exam, more flashing dots appeared in the same place as before. "It looks like you are reacting to the thought of your exam just as you did to me giving you an actual fright," said the Professor. "And, when this happens, it can stop the upper 'thinking' part of the brain from working properly, which means that we might struggle to think and talk about the very things that make us worried." When Rose asked why this happened, Arlo suggested that one or more bad experiences of tests had, perhaps, made her fearful of taking future ones, and that this way of thinking had got stronger and more powerful over time.

"Yes, I guess that makes sense," said Rose thoughtfully. "And I suppose that's why even though I know I am quite good at spell-casting, the fear of exams is making me, and my brain react this way.

"Exactly!" said Professor Jackdaw.

"I guess that's not something I can change, then, is it?" said Rose gloomily.

"Of course you can!" replied her black-clad teacher excitedly. "That's the wonderful thing about the brain, it's always re-wiring itself. Let me show you how. I don't suppose you know what getting grounded is, do you?"

R ose gave Arlo a cheeky smile before replying that she certainly did know what is was.

"Excellent," replied Professor Jackdaw, and continued, "well, let's give that a go first, shall we?"
Rose was not sure if that was a question or a statement but she started to do the activity she had learnt not half an hour ago with Arlo. She noticed that as she did it, she started to feel quite calm again. She also noticed that the mirror had stopped flashing so much.

"Excellent," said her professor again. "Now, just repeat

this sentence out loud: 'what's in the past I accept and let go, the future is new and my brain is too.'"

Rose repeated the sentence several times, and when she looked in the mirror again, the dots were a bit more spread out into the upper part of the brain.

"Wow!" she said "Was that a spell?"

"Nope," the Professor replied, "anyone can do it. You don't have to be a witch or a wizard. It's called a positive affirmation, but it works a bit like a spell. The new flashing dots suggest that your brain is behaving more logically and starting to let go of the fear from past events like Arlo just mentioned." Then the Professor explained that when we calm our brain down, it is possible to think more clearly and also to start to re-program our brain by thinking about things differently. By combining relaxation techniques with positive thinking, we can grow the good information signals and reduce the ones that make us feel bad.

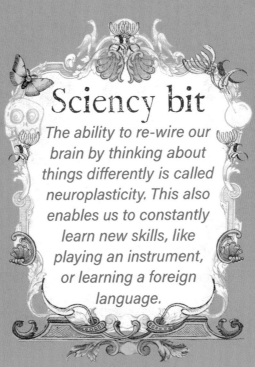

Sciency bit

The ability to re-wire our brain by thinking about things differently is called neuroplasticity. This also enables us to constantly learn new skills, like playing an instrument, or learning a foreign language.

"Thanks, Professor Jackdaw," said Arlo as he took Rose by the hand again and set off back down the hallway of mirrors.

"Where to now?"" asked Rose.

"Lunch, of course!"

As Arlo and Rose ate their lunch together, they talked about the latest sweets available at the school tuck shop and the forthcoming trip to Dengars Dragon Sanctuary. Rose was feeling a lot more relaxed now that she had found out about mindfulness and more about how her brain worked too. She was starting to wonder what else she could learn about managing her worries when their friend, Jade, wandered over to their table to say 'hi'. Jade was in the same year as Rose and often struggled with spell-casting. Rose thought she would probably be feeling nervous too so she asked her how she was feeling about their exam the next day. But Rose was rather surprised by her friend's answer.

"I'm feeling OK about it, thanks," said Jade. "I've been practising, you see."

"Practising your spell-casting, you mean?" said Rose.

"Well, yes, of course, but also my breathing," Jade replied. Rose gave her friend a quizzical look, so Jade suggested that Rose meet her in Professor Grindles' crystal ball room after lunch, and she would explain everything. Rose was sure that Jade was joking about the breathing practise, but decided to nip over to the crystal ball room just to make sure. After all, she thought, 'how great would it be to manage my anxiety just by using my breathing'!

When Rose entered Professor Grindles' room, she spotted Jade right away. Jade was sitting on a chair with her eyes closed and one hand on her chest, looking calm and peaceful. When Jade became aware of Rose, she opened her eyes and jumped up. She had a big smile on her face.

"I'm so pleased you came," she said, "come and have a look at this!"

Jade took Rose over to a wooden plinth with a large crystal ball on it and asked Rose to place her hand on it and think about tomorrow's exam. Rose did as she was asked, and as she did, a heart appeared inside the ball. It was beating rather fast.

"That's exactly what my heart used to do before I practised my breathing," said Jade. "Let me show you how to slow it down by using a simple trick called heart breathing."
Rose was starting to get a bit confused.

"Why would I want to slow it down?" she asked. "And what on earth is heart breathing?"
Jade explained that our hearts beat faster in response to fear, for example, a fear of exams. And that by slowing down the heart rate, you send a powerful message to the rest of the body that there is no actual danger, and that our body and brain can relax.

"That sounds amazing!" said Rose. "How do I do it?"
"Well, all you really need to do is learn how to blow out candles on a cake!" said Jade as she conjured up a cake with seven flickering candles on it.
Rose took some quick breaths and blew hard on the candles, blowing them out in two attempts. But she watched in dismay as they re-lit themselves within seconds and flickered as bright as before. She tried a few more times but the same thing kept happening and she was soon getting a bit dizzy and more than a little frustrated.

"Good effort," said Jade, "but there's a knack to using breathing to help manage anxiety. Rapid breaths like you've been doing, can actually make you feel more anxious and increase your heart rate, as well as making you feel dizzy. Try it like this. First, imagine you are blowing up a balloon in your belly as you take in a breath through your nose for four seconds. Then, imagine that you are blowing out through a straw and blow out slowly through your mouth for seven seconds. Have a practise, then try blowing out the candles using this way of breathing."

Rose had a few tries before giving the candles another go. This time they all went out first time, and, much to Rose's relief they stayed out.

"Right, then," said Jade excitedly, "I think you're ready to try the crystal ball again."

Jade took Rose back to the crystal ball and once again told her to place one hand on the ball and the other on her chest where she thought her heart was, and, if she was happy to do so, to close her eyes as well.

"Now do your candle breathing and imagine that you are breathing that air into and around your heart."

Rose did as she was told and was amazed by how calm and relaxed she felt, just by breathing in a different way. And when she opened her eyes, she saw the heart inside the crystal ball was beating nice and slowly. It also seemed to be glowing a lovely pink colour.

"Ah," said Jade, "I see you've discovered your calm colour. If you imagine this colour covering you from head to toe, it will help you become even more relaxed and be able to concentrate better. It's a bit like a superpower."

Rose gave it a go and, as she let the colour of pink swirl around her, she really did feel like she had a new super ability – the ability to feel calm, focussed and brave all at the same time.

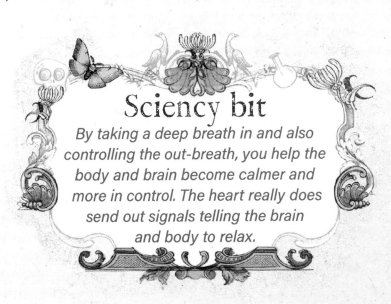

Sciency bit

By taking a deep breath in and also controlling the out-breath, you help the body and brain become calmer and more in control. The heart really does send out signals telling the brain and body to relax.

ose couldn't quite believe it, but after all these new tricks she had learnt, not only was she not feeling so nervous about the exam, but she was actually starting to look forward to it and the possibility that she could face her exam with curiosity instead of anxiety. After chatting to Jade about their exam, and thanking her for sharing her 'superpower', as well as eating a well-earned slice of cake together, Rose headed back to the library to do some reading before the school day ended.

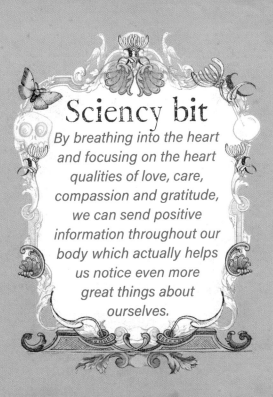

Sciency bit

By breathing into the heart and focusing on the heart qualities of love, care, compassion and gratitude, we can send positive information throughout our body which actually helps us notice even more great things about ourselves.

Later on, back at home, Rose told her parents and her brother all about her busy day and the wonderful things her friends and Professor Jackdaw had taught her about managing anxiety. They were very impressed and said that they would definitely try using those tips and tricks too.

Before bed Rose spent five minutes practising her heart breathing and then did her usual habit of writing down five things she was grateful for. This included her friends, her school and cuddles with her cat, Gwyneth. In the middle of night, Rose was woken up by a bad dream. But, after writing down the worries that woke her up, she used her new grounding and breathing tips to get back to sleep, and when her owl clock woke her up in the morning, she was feeling refreshed and in a great mood.

Sir Tapalot

Rose met Arlo at the fountain before school the following morning; the day of exam! She was excited about telling him that she had already been using all of the new tips and tricks she'd learnt the day before. But she also admitted that she was still feeling a little bit anxious about the exam. Arlo told her that most people, even him, feel a bit nervous before a test and that it's perfectly natural.

"I do have one more trick to show you, though," he said. "And I may have saved the best till last. Follow me!"

Arlo took Rose to the library, where Mrs Hanks, the librarian, was busy floating books back onto the correct shelves. She was obviously expecting them, as she ushered both pupils over to a table in the main hall, where small group of Year 7s were huddled together with their spell books doing some last-minute revision. Above the children was a large painting of a very well-dressed man. The plaque underneath it read, Sir Tapalot.

As the pair moved closer, the portrait started to move around before a deep voiced boomed,

"Ah, more students after my knowledge I see."

Rose knew the story of Sir Tapalot but had never, not even in her wildest dreams, thought that she would be having a conversation with him!

"Come along and sit down, you two, I can't hang around all day you know!" chuckled Sir Tapalot, amused at a joke that he had, no doubt, used on many occasions. "Now, Mrs Hanks has told me that you all have an exam today and that you may be having some yucky feelings about them."

'Yucky' was an understatement, Rose thought, but was nevertheless very interested in what Sir Tapalot was about to tell them.

"Lucky for you," Sir Tapalot continued, "I learnt a powerful trick centuries ago when, as a young wizard teacher, I was tasked with guarding this very school at night-time.

felt very anxious about this, I can tell you and, because actual magic was forbidden unless under extreme circumstances, I had to use non-magic to keep me calm and alert."

Sir Tapalot started off by asking all the young witches and wizards to think about the exam and then try to name the emotion they were feeling or where they felt yucky in their body or both if possible. He went on to ask them to rate how strongly they felt it from 0 to 10, 10 being the highest and 0 being not at all, before adding;

"Once you have noticed how you feel, come up here and write it on this ye-oldie blackboard." Everyone did as they were told, and Sir Tapalot went on to say that it was perfectly normal to have different reactions to other people, even if it's to the same thing.

"Marvellous!" cheered the flamboyant man from the

Feelings

Sir Tapalot

portrait. "Now, imagine your first two fingers are magic wands and follow me as we tap lightly on specific points on the body and see what happens."

Sir Tapalot proceeded to tap seven times on certain parts of his head and upper body. All the pupils, including Arlo, copied him.

After they had all done it, everyone agreed that the emotions they had felt before were not as strong now. In fact, they all felt so good, that they decided to do it a few more times to see what might happen. And after five minutes of tapping, Sir Tapalot asked everyone to rate their emotions again. This time the chalk board looked very different. Xavier, one of the Year 7 pupils, was especially impressed and said that he did not feel any of the anger he was feeling about the exam only a few minutes ago.

"It's funny, though," he said, "because I actually feel a bit sad now. Is that normal?"

Sir Tapalot explained that the tapping helps to release feelings of anxiety and anger, but that it can sometimes bring up other emotions too, and that these other emotions may also need to be tapped away in exactly the same way. Xavier did some more tapping and soon the feelings of sadness were gone as well.

Sciency bit

The proper name for tapping is 'Emotional Freedom Technique' (EFT). Tapping on certain points on the body sends a calming signal to the brain and more specifically the amygdala, a small part of the brain that's sends a warning signal to the body when it recognises a real or imagined danger.

The whole group really enjoyed the tapping activity, and everyone said they would tell all their friends about it. The spell books were then put away as the group chatted about the other techniques Rose had learnt the day before. After that, they headed to morning assembly, and all the way there, they were laughing together about the times their own spells had gone a bit topsy turvy!

"I suppose we all learn great lessons from our mistakes," giggled Rose. And everyone agreed that this was very true.

Later that day, as Rose headed to the Year 8 spell-casting exam, she passed her potions teacher in the hall, and he asked her how she was feeling. Rose paused for a minute and thought about all the things she had learnt over the last two days. Then she said, "I'm feeling really good, thank you." And she really was. In fact, she couldn't stop smiling.

The following year, at exam time, it was Rose's turn to pass on all her knowledge about how to cope with and manage anxiety and worries, and it is your turn too.

So, as you can see, these tricks and tips are not magic, but they work so well, they could be!

EFT Recap
How to use EFT/ 'Tapping'

1. Write down the problem that is making you anxious and how it's making you feel right now. This could be an emotion or a feeling in the body (for example butterflies in your stomach).

2. Make a note of how intensely you feel this between 0 (lowest) and 10 (highest).

3. Tap on the side of the hand with your fingertips and say what is bothering you right now followed by one or more of the following statements
"I love and accept myself", " I deeply and completely accept myself"
"I am doing the best I can", "I am OK", "I will be OK"

For example: "The test tomorrow is making me feel anxious. I feel a bit sick in my throat and rate it at 7 but I am doing the best I can, and I will be OK"

4. Tap lightly on all the points mentioned below 7 times as you do one round of tapping. Make sure you wash your hands beforehand and miss out any points you don't want to use.

- Top of head
- Eyebrow point
- Side of the eye
- Under the eye
- Under the nose
- Under the chin
- On the collarbone
- Under the arm
- On the side of each finger tip

5. After one round of tapping, go back to your notes and write down how you are feeling about that problem now.

6. Keep going until the intensity goes down to a low score, for example 1 or 2 or even a 0 which means it has gone completely.